SIN CITY FABLES

written by **Alfa-Betty Olsen** & **Marshall Efron**
illustrated by **Steven Guarnaccia**
produced by **Steven Heller**

A & W PUBLISHERS · NEW YORK

ABOUT THE AUTHORS

They have been writing together since 1971 when they were a part of PBS' Emmy-winning Great American Dream Machine. Since then they have written several books, Marshall Efron's Illustrated, Simplified, and Painless Sunday School, (CBS' award-winning Children's program for adults); and written for the movies. This book is their favorite work so far; they are well-suited to the subject. Miss Olsen's humor credentials are impeccable: she has an unbending literal mind and often hears things wrong. Mr. Efron has urban credentials that are above reproach: he takes rubbings of derelicts for a hobby and vacations by tenting out in Central Park, unarmed.

ABOUT THE ILLUSTRATOR

Steven Guarnaccia's illustrations and drawings have been seen in The New York Times, New York Magazine, The Boston Globe, Esquire, and numerous other publications in the United States and Europe. He has brought an invaluable sensibility to this book in that he commits sins on a daily basis and repents during working hours. His confessions to the police are long and tedious, and they are considered to be of no value.

ACKNOWLEDGEMENTS

We wish to thank John Engels, Ruth Pollack, Sarah Jane Freymann, Steven Schwartz, Cindy Lake, Lucie Binger, and Jean Behrend for their invaluable help with this book.

Published by
A & W Publishers, Inc.
95 Madison Avenue
New York, New York 10016
Designed by Steven Heller
Library of Congress Number: 80-70374
ISBN: 0-89104-205-9
Printed in the United States of America.

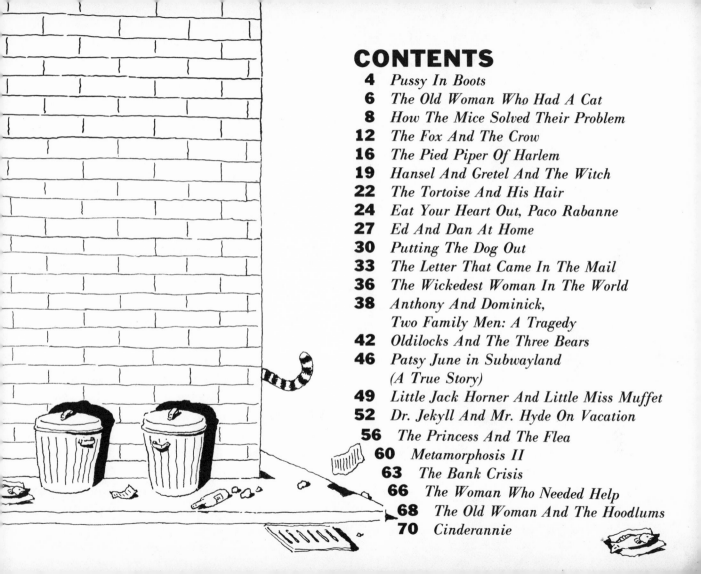

CONTENTS

4 *Pussy In Boots*

6 *The Old Woman Who Had A Cat*

8 *How The Mice Solved Their Problem*

12 *The Fox And The Crow*

16 *The Pied Piper Of Harlem*

19 *Hansel And Gretel And The Witch*

22 *The Tortoise And His Hair*

24 *Eat Your Heart Out, Paco Rabanne*

27 *Ed And Dan At Home*

30 *Putting The Dog Out*

33 *The Letter That Came In The Mail*

36 *The Wickedest Woman In The World*

38 *Anthony And Dominick,*
Two Family Men: A Tragedy

42 *Oldilocks And The Three Bears*

46 *Patsy June in Subwayland*
(A True Story)

49 *Little Jack Horner And Little Miss Muffet*

52 *Dr. Jekyll And Mr. Hyde On Vacation*

56 *The Princess And The Flea*

60 *Metamorphosis II*

63 *The Bank Crisis*

66 *The Woman Who Needed Help*

68 *The Old Woman And The Hoodlums*

70 *Cinderannie*

PUSSY IN BOOTS

 miller, dying of starvation because no one can make a living milling these days now that the large giants have taken all the contracts and executed them, divided his property up among his three sons. He loved his three sons equally, but he loved his third son, Norell, the least equal and that is why he gave his oldest son the useless mill, his second son the useless ass and his third son, Norell, who was gay, had to content himself with the useless cat, Mary Madeline.

Norell was not at all upset. He left his two brothers to wailing and gnashing their teeth and took Mary Madeline and hit the streets. "This may come as a surprise to some, but I know just what to do with a good pussy," he said. "There's a very old saying, 'A cat can hook for a queen.'" He bought Mary Madeline a pair of sleazy high-heeled boots and some really rotten perfume, and put her on a corner, and her favors up for sale.

The cat became known as Pussy in Boots and Norell, who with the proceeds of Mary Madeline's efforts had bought himself a bright red suit of clothing, dubbed himself The Scarlett Pimp Norell. Norell thought he was a really clever entrepreneur. He even tried expanding with Ewe in Boots, Cow in Boots, and Nanny Goat in Boots, but they didn't work out. The market was too small.

Now the cat, who had always been a slut but never a bitch (she was no dog), took to the life in a big way. She went into heat very often, especially in the winter, and that made her very popular. She was only arrested once, and that was when she had kittens. Littering in the streets, as everyone knows, is illegal. Everything was going really well. Then Mary Madeline, in an excess of enthusiasm, started giving it away and the street competition killed her and Norell.

MORAL: *Never Send a Cat on a Woman's Errand.*

THE OLD WOMAN WHO HAD A CAT

here was once a very old woman who lived by herself with her cat. She loved her cat very, very much. Then the cat died and she was alone. The old woman felt very, very sad. She was also very, very angry. "It's no good to love something," she thought to herself. "I've wasted my time with that cat." And she swore that she would never have another cat. So she went out and bought a rat because, as she put it, "Nobody cares when a rat dies."

MORAL: *Sometimes What Is Good for You Is Unhealthy.*

7

HOW THE MICE SOLVED THEIR PROBLEM

 ife had become harsh and cruel and increasingly dangerous for the mice living in one of the newer subsidized housing developments for lower-income families. Oh yes, in the beginning, when the ribbon was cut and the buildings were opened for occupancy, mice came from all over, rejoicing that finally modern engineering had provided them with air-conditioning duct roadways that really worked, but that had been a while ago.

For years these mice had flourished and multiplied, but then some troublemaking Fascist had politically organized the human population of the buildings, and as a result a concerted effort to eliminate the rodent population had taken place. Some of the most deadly poisons known to man and mouse had cut their number down by more than half and that, combined with the assault of the sterilized but very sexy mice, which had brought about nearly zero population growth, had decimated the once-thriving community. Mourning wreaths were up everywhere and the remaining survivors were afflicted with a deep and numbing depression.

It has been said that the future belongs to the young and Daniel Founder, a young ambitious mouse, who had just begun to live, and who didn't want to die just yet, looked out at the world from between the door and the sill and decided that there was a big world out there and maybe a place for a better life. He said good-bye to his family and padded out.

Daniel Founder wasn't quite sure what he was looking for, but he believed he would know it when he saw it. Two weeks out he saw it and he knew it—The Nature's Way Whole Earth Food Center: "No Preservatives, No Artificial Flavors, No Additives, No Colorings, No Poisons of Any Kind." Immediately he scampered back to the few who were left in the place of his birth and gathered up those who would leave with him, his Mom, his Dad, and his fiancée, Louise. They migrated.

At first it was only the four of them; then there were the sixteen of them; then the ninety-

9

eight of them; then the two hundred and fourteen of them; and then the three thousand, six hundred and fourteen of them; and then the three thousand, six hundred and twenty of them; and the living was easy. There was plenty for everyone—an overabundance of the good things of life: tofu-imitation egg salad, tofu-imitation chopped liver, Yorba Buena soya steaks, meatless meatballs, sugarless sweetener, sweetened honey, and the mysterious but irresistible mustard eclairs. Life was great and so was the company.

Enter the cat. One day Mouse Scott was missing. He didn't show up for sleep. The next day Tootsie Puhl, Damen Hunnicutt, and Mr. Cheese were gone. On the third night R. L. Hutchison spotted the cat. Case closed. Mystery solved. They knew what was happening.

Leo Stein, who had always been political, called for a mass meeting of all the mice. He chaired the assembly.

"Fellow mice," he said, "you know how serious our situation is. I don't have to tell you. This meeting was called for the purpose of proposing ideas for a solution. Does anyone have a plan or a suggestion or a what-have-you?"

Sonny Boydecker raised a paw. "This situation is ridiculous," he squeaked. Everyone agreed.

Hillary Nehrenberg caught the attention of the chair and was recognized. "We are mice," she said, and all the mice agreed with a quiet murmur, "but what about the pigeons? I think they should be involved. After all, is not the cat their enemy, too?"

Mildred Whiskers couldn't stand this suggestion. "Pigeons!" she said. "Pigeons are dirty. Pigeons are nothing more than flying vermin."

"What's wrong with vermin?" shouted Sylvia Citron. "What do you think *we* are? Pigs?"

"This is ridiculous," squeaked Sonny Boydecker.

"The problem is the cat," shouted Leo Stein. "What about the cat?"

The Three Blind Mice: Hear-No-Evil, See-No-Evil, and Squeak-No-Evil stood up. "It seems to us we have to kill the cat. Let's get a gun and shoot the bastard dead."

Leo Stein called for a vote. All the mice voted. They were unanimously agreed. They then shot the cat dead and lived happily ever after.

MORAL: *Democracy Works.*

THE FOX AND THE CROW

t was the end of the year, and there was to be a New Year's party at the stock-broking offices of B. F. Mutton. Sid Bull (PhD., Econ., London School of Economics, 1956) was in charge of the hors d'oeuvres and the ice; Bud Bear (BFA, Rhode Island School of Design, 1961; MA, Bus. Admin., NYU 1964), the crepe paper; Sonja-The-Wise-Old Owl (BA, Bus. Admin., CCNY, 1939), the confetti and the party hats.

All year Bernard Fox (BA, Yale, Poli. Sci., 1972) had been going on about certain crows, street-smart survivors that he knew of, who were really into the good stuff, and it was therefore agreed by an almost unanimous decision of the Board of Directors that he would be the one to procure the drugs for the party.

On Christmas Eve Bernard went to Union Square Park late in the afternoon. The crows were all hanging out around the entrance, and on all the benches near the equestrian statue and beyond. They were, in fact, all over the park.

"Good," thought Bernard. "Supply is up and demand is down. That means lower prices for me. I can buy low to get high."

As Bernard walked up to a particularly furtive-looking crow who was perched on the lowest limb of a particularly furtive-looking tree (it was hiding behind the comfort station), he decided to apply the first rule of negotiation: Flatter your opponent. "Hey, my man," he said, smiling. "I can see by your threads that you know what's hip. You are right there, my bird. Where there is action, there is you. And where there is you, there is action. You are danger and spice. I bet you get a lot of action off the chicks. There is something wild and untamed about you. Bird, you reek of animal," said Bernard. "I'm on a strict budget, but I want a lot of what's good."

"I got the good that'll get you on," said the crow (DO*, PS 81, 1975).

13

"How can I be sure it's the real McCoy?" asked Bernard, getting into the second stage of negotiation: Put your opponent's pride on the line.

"It got that cat over there so high, he's laid low," said the crow. Bernard looked and saw a large Manx cat flat on his side and happily conscious.

"I'll take that stuff," said Bernard, "and I'll take a discount for paying cash." He was into the final step of negotiation: Ask for something outrageous—you might get it.

"I can only give you five percent," said the crow, "this is the best drug on the market."

"It's a deal," said Bernard.

He filled his portfolio and returned to Wall Street. By this time the office was very festive indeed. The crepe paper was hung, the paper hats had been distributed, and the entire staff was armed with his or her very own noisemaker.

Bernard passed out his drug supply, along with seasonal green and red rolling papers, and they all rolled their own joy sticks and lit up.

Not much happened. Hardly anyone got high. Only Jim Jackass (BA, MA, Wharton School of Bus., 1958) was stoned. "How do you know you're high?" someone asked him. "I can't

kick," he replied. "Also I perceive spatial disorientation and I have an insatiable craving for peanut brittle."

"You are a jackass," said Lenny Cat-Snake (BA, Marketing, Princeton, 1976), Bernard's hated office mate. "If this stuff isn't catnip, my name isn't Cat-Snake. I was afraid something like this would happen and I've taken the precaution of providing a fallback alternative. Basically, I went to my dealer, a cat named Cosy Nostra, a really classy and reliable type, who wears alligator shoes and a real gold wristwatch, and he sold me this!" Lenny brought forth a lovely old fruitcake tin with a nostaligc scene from Dickens' *Oliver Twist* on it (Fagin teaching the boys how to pick pockets). He opened it and passed around the already rolled joints that it contained. The office lit up. The office had a terrific party except, of course, Jim Jackass, who suffered a paranoid episode.

Meanwhile, back in the park, the crow and all his friends dressed up and went uptown to Cosy Nostra's office party. The crow bought the hors d'oeuvres.

MORAL: *A Very Merry Christmas Was Had by All Because During the Holiday Season There Is Never Just One Party.*

THE PIED PIPER OF HARLEM

There was once a man who *really* loved his portable radio, a PanDemonic 720X with all the bands, eight giant speakers, a built-in woofer, a built-in tweeter, an echo reverb, Dolby, digital readout, and four knobs on the side that had no purpose discernible to any earthling. He played it on the subway while chain-smoking cigarettes; he played it on the street while drinking wine; he even played it in the movies during the feature while eating noisy crunchy things out of a crisp cellophane bag. He especially liked to play it while walking through residential areas at 2 o'clock in the morning and also near hospitals. He played it loud and this meant he always spoke at the top of his lungs in order to be heard.

He was not well liked. His mother hated him. Women shunned him. Men and boys alike crossed the street when they saw him coming. His name was Lydell and he lived in Harlem and he was known around his neighborhood as the Pied Piper of Harlem because the one living species that he attracted were rats, rats who loved to boogie to the beat of his bop machine, and they followed him everywhere.

This meant he had never held down a job for more than a day. His appointment as the superintendent of a slum apartment building lasted a half hour and during that space of time his life was threatened eleven times by the tenants and he increased the rat population of the building by 300. As a night watchman he lasted only ten minutes because he was arrested by the police for disturbing the police.

Lydell's life was a river of sadness fed by a steady stream of rejection, and each time Lydell suffered a rebuff he drew closer to his radio, his only friend. The most depressing part of this was that Lydell thought he was doing the world a favor. He thought he was making life an ongoing party. He looked upon people who used earphones with their radios as selfish. Whenever he was with his radio, which was always, he was happy. Why then, he wondered, was he

17

so miserable?

He applied to the city for help and was referred to a Dr. Barry Plotkin, a psychiatric therapist with much experience working with alienated individuals. Dr. Plotkin saw Lydell several times and listened to Lydell shouting his problems over the blaring radio, while rats (almost a hundred of them) danced all over his office. And Dr. Plotkin told Lydell that he, Lydell, had chosen an inappropriate love object and that this was ruining his life. Lydell's problems, he gently screamed, stemmed from his unnatural attachment to his radio. He suggested that Lydell try finding a more suitable love object.

Lydell tried to fall in love with an elevator. He tried furniture. He tried a neon sign, a refrigerator, an oven, a slot machine, a cappucino maker, a manhole cover. Nothing worked. He realized then that he was a one-radio man. He took his radio out of the closet, dusted it off, turned it on, and instantly knew contentment, satisfaction, and that wonderful sense of completeness that only comes with true love. He was also immediately surrounded by rats.

MORAL: *Wherever There Is Music, There Are Dancing Feet.*

HANSEL AND GRETEL AND THE WITCH

nce upon a time in the summer a woodcutter and his family were having a hard time of it for no one seemed to want firewood. Their refrigerator was empty and they didn't know what they were going to do.

"Let's get rid of the kids," suggested the woodcutter's wife.

"You're right dear," said the woodcutter. "I love Hansel and Gretel but what you say makes sense, and maybe if things get better we can have more kids."

The next day the woodcutter took the children into a part of the city that was so old and run-down that no one lived there anymore. "Now, wait here while I go away. I love you," he said and disappeared.

"Gee, Dad never spoke to us like that before," said Hansel.

"I bet we've been abandoned," said Gretel.

"The bastard," said Hansel with a touch of anger.

"I'm getting hungry," said Gretel. "Have you ever noticed how hungry you get when you've been abandoned?"

"Yes," said Hansel.

It grew dark and they went to sleep. The next day Hansel kept saying to Gretel, "Don't worry, we will find our way back." They walked for blocks in all directions but to no avail. They grew hungrier. Soon they were so tired they could not drag themselves along, so they lay down under some old cardboard boxes and went to sleep again.

It was now the morning of the third day since they had left their father's house, and still they walked on, but they never saw any buildings that were familiar or occupied. Hansel saw that if they did not eat soon they would die of hunger.

Then when it was noon they saw a fat old pigeon that was moulting, sitting upon an aban-

19

doned Lark that was rusting. It (the pigeon) cocked its head and looked at them with one of its eyes, then spread its wings and flew off, dropping feathers as it went. Hansel and Gretel followed the trail of feathers. The pigeon led them to a cookie stand manned by an old crone who wore a pointed black hat, a long black dress, shoes that curled up at the toes and under the heels, and who had a long pointed nose with a gigantic wart with a hair in it at the tip. She was typical of her race and she was selling Weird Sister's Gingerbread Cookies made at home in her own cauldron.

The two children looked forlorn and begged some cookies from the soft-hearted hellhag. She gave them two big ones. They took two bites, one bite per child per cookie.

"Oh my God, I've been poisoned," said Gretel.

Hansel just lay on the ground and writhed. In his pain he forgot all language.

"What did you put in these?" gasped Gretel.

"Milk of tuna, dried puppy lining, goat balls, mouse oil, moth hair, and a couple of drops of spider sweat," said the witch. "It's an old LeFay family recipe."

Hansel and Gretel eventually did find their way home and gave the rest of their cookies to their parents, who did not like them either.

MORAL: *Ethnic Food Is Not for Everyone.*

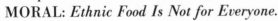

THE TORTOISE AND HIS HAIR

Mel was a very unhappy tortoise. He was naturally gifted. He could dance, he could sing, he could make the most entrancing small talk a body ever listened to. He even knew wine—when to serve it and when to throw it away and not keep it in the refrigerator any longer. But, he could never get a girl. When he went to singles' bars looking, they turned their backs on him. The reason: Mel had no hair. He was as bald as the dome of St. Peter's in Rome. Women would look at him and barf. "Yuuuuuuooooooocehhhhh! Cchhaa! Pui!" was the kindest thing ever said to him. Behind his back it was worse.

Mel took the plunge, head first, into hair transplants and after several months he faced the world from under a veritable jungle of curly black hair. And it worked. Mel could not keep the women away. His phone rang from dawn to dusk and well into the night. Of course he was not the same Mel. The treatments had damaged his small brain, and he'd forgotten everything he'd known including how to think; but nobody cared, least of all Mel. He was happy. He had women.

MORAL: *Vanity Is Not in Vain Because Beauty Is Everything.*

23

EAT YOUR HEART OUT, PACO RABANNE

*H*E was beautiful: seven inches long, darting black eyes, an exquisite tapered body that came to a point, and a brilliant blue-forked tongue that danced out from his mouth full of vitality and life. He was chic. He was sophisticated. He was a lounge lizard to be reckoned with.

SHE was cute and fluffy: whiskers that throbbed with come hither appeal, saucy green eyes, a delicate pink nose, a rotund little body, a seductive waddling walk and a low pitched purr no male could resist. She was soft. She was feminine. She was the ultimate sex kitten.

HE had seen her around and had checked her out and she had let him know from the way she carried her tail that she was entertaining at least a passing interest in his flame.

SHE telephoned.

HE answered.

"Hello?"

"Eddie?"

"Yes?"

"It's me. Twinkie."

"Yes?"

"We met last week. At the watering hole. You were trying to rub me the right way."

"I was only trying to get rid of the loose hairs."

"In a pig's eye. You were trying to mount me. You blushed when I caught you at it."

"I change color on purpose. It's part of my chameleon charm."

"I'd like to see you."

"I, too."

"I have a bowl of curdled old milk, some soggy cat chow, and a mellow litter box. Would

you like to come over?"

"For such an elegant invitation, I will dust my scales, polish my eyes and then I will take some Sap de Pine Tree, which is a most elegant cologne, and I will place it on several parts of my body, after which my dear Twinkle. . . ."

"The name is Twinkie. And if you step on it, I'll put out some honey and catch a few flies."

HE was there in a flash, thoroughly smitten.

SHE played hard to get.

"Before I let you get it on with me, how do I know that you are sincere?"

"Wait. I'll shed my skin for you."

HE did so.

SHE thought his hide made a perfect handbag.

They were married and lived happily ever after, and every year Eddie gave Twinkie a new lizard skin.

26   **MORAL:** *No Matter What the Ads Say, Scaly Skin Is Attractive.*

ED AND DAN AT HOME

an and Ed were two accountants who shared an apartment. One night Dan's mother called and told him that there was a full moon that night and suggested that the boys stay home for the evening. Dan told Ed, and Ed thought it was a good idea; and so they both settled down for a quiet sit by the fire. Dan began doing the crossword puzzle, and Ed started reading a report for Mr. Muller, his boss. Then Dan broke the tip of his pencil, became very upset, and started crying. Ed asked Dan what the trouble was, and Dan told him.

"In that case," said Ed, "I shall tear the pages of this report into tiny little bits."

The phone rang. It was Mr. Muller wanting the information from the report. "I'm sorry, Mr. Muller," said Ed. "I can't give you the information because Dan was upset over breaking the point on his pencil, so I tore up the report. It was the only copy."

Mr. Muller said, "In that case I am going to rip the telephone out of the wall by its wires and throw it out the window."

The phone went through the cloth top of the Fiat Spyder Bruce was driving and hit him on the head, rendering him dizzy.

"Why did you throw the phone out the window?" said Bruce to Mr. Muller.

Mr. Muller said, "Because Ed tore up the report with the information I needed when Dan broke the point on his pencil."

"In that case," said Bruce, "I shall drive into those three parked cars."

Officer Pepys came onto the scene while the smoke was still in the air and the oil and water still dripping from the four ruined cars. "What have you done here?" he asked.

"Not my fault, sir," explained Bruce. "You see, I was driving along minding my business when I was beaned on the head by a telephone thrown by Mr. Muller over there on the third floor, who was irate because he couldn't get the information he needed from one of his asso-

27

ciates, who had torn up the only copy of the report because his friend Dan had broken the point of his pencil doing a crossword puzzle."

"Not a good excuse," said Officer Pepys. "I'll have to shoot myself and call out the SWAT Team."

The SWAT Team arrived, and Officer Pepys, with his last few breaths, told them that he had shot himself because Bruce had run into three parked cars because Mr. Muller had ripped his phone out of the wall and thrown it out the window right through Bruce's car's canvas top because Ed had torn up the only copy of the report he was reading because Dan had broken the tip of his pencil doing a crossword puzzle.

    The SWAT Team shot up the neighborhood until they were shot up by the National Guard, who were quelled by the regular army. This alerted the Russians, who atom-bombed their own cities. The Chinese, who were under the Russian fallout, destroyed their famous wall. The Japanese committed national *hara-kiri*, a huge tidal wave destroyed California, and Mount St. Helens erupted again.

MORAL: *It's Not Even Safe to Stay at Home When the Moon Is Full.*

PUTTING THE DOG OUT

fter having been on the waiting list for six and a half years, Mrs. Edna Bronte, a middle-class widow, was finally able to rent the apartment of her dreams: a six-room penthouse duplex atop a middle-class apartment building that contained both rent-controlled and rent-stabilized apartments. The apartment had wonderful terraces on all sides and afforded a breathtaking view of the city and numerous points of entry for the enterprising burglar. Mrs. Bronte was afraid, and so she bought a killer dog to protect herself. The dog's name was Orca.

Late one night Orca encountered an unauthorized person on the terrace with the northeast view. True to his breed, his blood, and his expensive training, Orca leapt upon the intruder and killed him on the spot. He grabbed the inert and lifeless form of the burglar and shook him viciously, growling all the time. Then he took the body and lifted it up and threw it down. He did this over and over again. Orca was having a heck of a good time.

The commotion awakened Mrs. Bronte who, peering fearfully through the blinds, saw her killer pet playfully mauling the body of a stranger.

Mrs. Bronte was revolted, shocked and disturbed. She had not reckoned with this grizzly truth. She had not expected that Orca would actually do that thing which he had been born and bred to do: kill.

There was nothing else to do. Mrs. Bronte called the police. "Have you tied and muzzled the dog yet?" asked Officer Meyer. "No," replied Mrs. Bronte. "He's a police dog." "I tell you what, lady," said Officer Meyer. "You hang up your phone now, and you go out on your terrace, and you tie up your dog. And then you pick up your phone, and you call me back, and I'll send a car around. Otherwise I can't in good conscience dispatch any men."

Mrs. Bronte looked out the window again. Orca was happily gnawing on the head of the

31

burglar. This time she called the Canine Behavioral Modifier who had trained Orca and guaranteed him. "Orca has killed a man and now I don't know what to do," she began her complaint.

"I am certain," said Herman Regensteiner, interrupting her in his continental way, "that if Orca killed a man he had a very good reason for doing so." Then he hung up.

Mrs. Bronte parted the blinds and looked out at Orca again, reassured as to his character. Orca put one paw possessively upon what was left of the burglar's chest, growled, and bared his teeth at Mrs. Bronte to let her know that this was his kill, his victim, and she was not to try and take it away. Mrs. Bronte stared at him for a full minute, then she closed the blinds and went about her life.

Eventually Orca ate all of the burglar, except for his shoes and a few stray tools, and began to bark and ask to be let in again. Mrs. Bronte was adamant. She would not let Orca into the house. This went on for about a week. The neighbors complained. Mrs. Bronte was ticketed by the ASPCA for abusing an animal and received another ticket from the police for creating a nuisance and disturbing the peace.

Finally Mrs. Bronte gave in to the pitiful whining and scratching at the door and let Orca into the house again. Orca crawled toward her, belly on the floor. Her heart melted. She gave him a doggie treat and from then on Mrs. Bronte and Orca lived together harmoniously . . . until the next burglar.

MORAL: *When Your Dog Gets the Upper Hand, He Rules Your Life.*

THE LETTER THAT CAME IN THE MAIL

rnie Hansen, who had been living as nicely as a passive-aggressive personality can live, received a rather startling letter one day in the mail. The first part of the letter took the form of a prayer: "Trust in the Lord with all your heart, for He is all-powerful and loves you." It went on to wish everybody in the world good health, good luck, and riches. The letter instructed him to mail $5.00 to the first name on a list that was ten names long, to send ten copies of the letter to ten friends, *but*, and this was the alarming part of the request, he was to leave off the first name on the list and add his own name to the bottom. Ultimately, the letter promised, he would move up the list to the first position and then he would receive a great deal of money in the mail. Money beyond his wildest dreams. Arnie didn't like it. He also felt that he was being threatened. The reason he felt that he was being threatened was that he was being threatened.

"General Braverman received this letter, disregarded it, and two days later led his troops into quicksand.

"Movie star, Wayne Kellogg, received this letter and used it to light his barbecue at his Malibu Beach Colony home. The very next night as he stepped up to receive the Oscar for portraying Larry in *The Endless Afternoon*, in front of millions of TV viewers, he was attacked by static cling and this ended his career.

"Dr. Carlos Pectin was about to perform a simple tonsillectomy on a healthy twelve-year-old. Just minutes before he stepped into the operating room, he hacked this letter to shreds. Needless to say, the patient died due to negligence on Pectin's part. The boy's parents sued Pectin and collected. Pectin was ruined and now works as a substitute surgeon."

Arnie did mail out ten copies of the letter just as it instructed, but, to inconvenience and hopefully irritate *them*, whoever *they* were, he misspelled all the names and addresses, includ-

ing his own. He never received any money and complained about this endlessly.

One day Arnie Hansen developed a tickle in his throat. This led to soreness that would not stop. This led to fever. Arnie checked into the hospital. He was told he needed an operation; and just as he was being put under, he was told that his doctor couldn't make it, and that Dr. Pectin would be his substitute doctor. The last thing that Arnie saw was the wild-eyed Dr. Pectin bearing down on him and then the lights went out.

MORAL: *It Is Better to Be a Manic-Depressive Like Dr. Pectin Than a Passive-Aggressive Like Arnie Hansen.*

THE WICKEDEST WOMAN IN THE WORLD

The name of the wickedest woman in the world was Lillian Smallwood and hers is a terrible tale. She was very, very bad. Her behavior was incredibly shocking. The neighbors gossiped endlessly; and her husband, Arnold Smallwood, lived in constant fear that she would be carted off by the police.

Lillian Smallwood was four pounds overweight, and yet every morning she could not stop herself but put sugar and milk into her coffee and then drank it! Oh, she was contrite enough, and she apologized (endlessly) but she could not be trusted.

Some days she ate a chocolate-chip cookie alone in the kitchen before the children came home from school. The children sensed this, and although she would lie to them, they knew better. The poor little things were hollow-eyed and weak from shame and horror.

She grew in her evil. There were times when she did not make it to exercise class. And she had been known to stop in strange coffee shops and indulge herself with a hot English muffin dabbed with butter and grape jelly, all the time apologizing to the waitress. Other customers would draw away from her in horror.

Her best friends, Linda Shaffer, Eve Darcy, and Theresa Ann Garr, had to be hospitalized for shock after she ordered the chocolate mousse at the end of lunch one afternoon. "You'll forgive me," she said. But they couldn't. Not until their last breath.

She finally touched bottom the day she had three Triskets straight from the box and a handful of cashews. As she ate she said, "Dear God, I'm beyond redemption." No sooner were the words out of her mouth than a goblin came and took her away to hell where a place was reserved for her in the confectionery. There she was forced to eat French cooking and many dainty desserts, and feel guilty about it for all of eternity.

MORAL: *The Road to Hell Is Paved with Goodies.*

ANTHONY AND DOMINICK, TWO FAMILY MEN: A TRAGEDY

nce upon a time there were two men who belonged to the same family—a family that did not officially exist, except in the movies, on television, in the pages of sleazy tabloids and respectable newspapers, and the files of the Justice Department, the FBI, and Interpol. One was named Dominick and the other was named Anthony. They were both mature men in their seventies, and chubby. Both were married, and both loved their respective blood relations very much. Dominick had a son who was a doctor, and Anthony had a daughter who was a social worker. Neither man had ever cheated on his wife.

The two of them met every Thursday night in the back room of Vito's Fish Grotto (home of fine steaks) to go over certain important family business: who should sit where at what tables, who needed a warning, and who needed a haircut. They had been doing this for thirty years and took turns paying the check.

One night, because he had made a killing during the week, Dominick wanted to pick up the check even though it wasn't his turn. After a well-prepared meal of antipasto, fettuccine Alfredo, spaghettini con vongole, gnocchi, calamare, minestrone, osso buco, scallopine, two small dishes of corn, insalata mista, zuppa Inglese, baba rhum, and cannoli (chocolate and pistachio), as the two men were leaning back in their chairs, munching amaretto cookies and sipping double espressos, Dominick broached the subject.

"This has been a very good week for me," said Dominick, "a very good week. I would like to pick up the tab for tonight's dinner."

"It has been a good week for me, too," said Anthony, "a very good week. And I will pick up

39

the tab because it is my turn. That is the way it has always been and that is the way it is. So be it."

"No, no, no," said Dominick. "Look, I had half your salad and most of your zuppa Inglese. Please allow me the courtèsy of the gesture, at least."

"No, no, no, my dear Dominick," said Anthony. "My honor demands I pay for dinner and you know how I prize my honor."

"I got honor, too," asserted Dominick. He called over the waiter and shoved handfuls of money into the waiter's pockets. Anthony looked on darkly, brooding, angry.

When they had left the restaurant and were out on the sidewalk, under the stars, and the streetlights, Anthony pulled a knife and stabbed Dominick. "This will teach you to pay for my

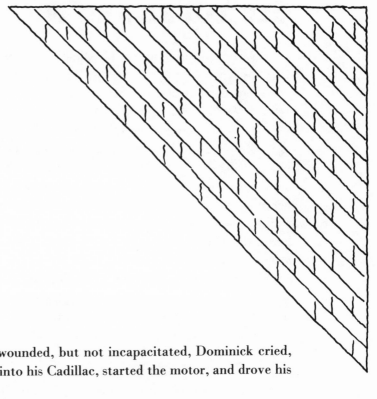

dinner," he said. Now greatly insulted and wounded, but not incapacitated, Dominick cried, "Look what you did to my jacket!" jumped into his Cadillac, started the motor, and drove his car at Anthony full speed ahead.

Anthony had been enraged before, but when he was hit by the car, and thrown up onto its hood, his anger escalated. He pulled a gun and shot Dominick point blank through the windshield and into the face. The car continued going until it plowed into the wall of a brick building and pulverized Anthony.

MORAL: *The National Enquirer Is Right. Eating Corn Does Lead to Violence.*

OLDILOCKS AND THE THREE BEARS

nflation had hit Oldilocks in the pocketbook and the blow was nearly fatal. What's more, she did not qualify for food stamps, Medicare, Social Security, or welfare. She was too poor. Desperate, she attempted a life of crime. Oldilocks got herself a forty-five and took to the dark alleys and the neglected cross streets near the grimy, pathetic doorway she called home.

The forty-five was too heavy for her to carry around for very long, so she put a string on it and dragged it. This made it hard for her to mug people. Those she did manage to point the muzzle at laughed at her and, truth to be told, Oldilocks did not have the nerve to pull the trigger. She was afraid it might hurt her.

She gave up mugging and tried being a cat burglar. The cats scratched her and tried to bury her in their boxes. Oldilocks was in trouble. She ended up as a sneak thief and went through apartment houses trying doors.

One day she stumbled into an apartment that belonged to three bears—big Daddy Bear, medium-sized Mamma Bear, and tiny Baby Bear. The Bear family was out for a walk. They had left their door unlocked because they were new in town and stupid.

The first thing that struck Oldilocks' eyes in the apartment was the table that was set for lunch. There were three bowls of porridge on that table and Oldilocks tried them all. The first bowl was very large and the porridge in it was too hot. Oldilocks ate it anyway and moved on to the next bowl of porridge—the medium-sized bowl of porridge. It was too cold for Oldilocks, but she ate it all up anyway. She was a woman who liked her porridge. She moved to the third bowl of porridge—the tiny one. It was just right. Oldilocks ate the entire bowl and cleaned it with her tongue. That tired her out, so she decided to sit down for a minute and catch her breath.

First she tried the big chair that belonged to Daddy Bear. It was too hard for her. She

43

didn't like it. Then she tried the medium-sized chair that belonged to Mamma Bear. It was too soft. She didn't like it. Then she tried the tiny chair that belonged to Baby Bear. She liked the chair, but she broke it and it was no good to sit in any more. Falling through the bottom of the baby chair had tired her even more, and she wandered into the bedroom, where, to her surprise, she found three beds.

She tried the big bed that belonged to Daddy Bear, but it was too big and gave her an anxiety attack. She felt lost in it. Then she tried the bed that belonged to Mamma Bear, but there were too many pillows on it, and she felt as though she was still sitting up although lying down; so she tried the bed that belonged to Baby Bear and it was too short for her, but she fell asleep anyway.

The three Bears came home. First they saw that the porridge had been eaten up. Then they saw that their chairs had been tampered with. Then they saw that their beds had been messed up. And then they saw Oldilocks. She was snoring silently.

The three Bears did not have the nerve to call the police and have an old woman arrested, so they woke her up instead and politely asked her to leave. Oldilocks looked at them. She looked at their big furry bodies. She looked at their long muzzles with big, wet, shiny, healthy bear noses at the ends. She looked at their big, compassionate bear eyes. "You're bears aren't you?" she said. "Yes, we are," replied Daddy Bear. "What of it?" "Does your landlord know that bears are living in this apartment?" Oldilocks continued. "Not exactly," hedged Daddy Bear. "Just as I thought," said Oldilocks. "Animals cannot legally rent apartments and that's

44

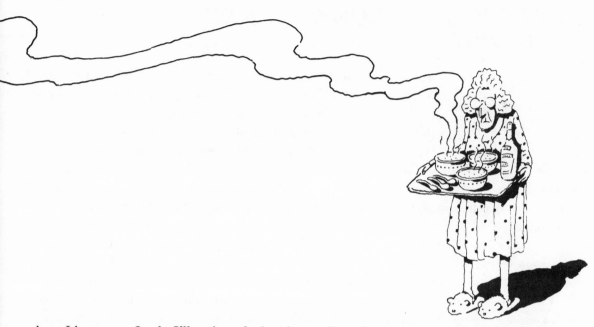

where I have you. Look, I'll make a deal with you. I won't turn you in to the landlord. Instead I'll front for you. I'll pretend that this is my apartment, and I'll live here with you."

The Bears did not like it, but they understood that they had no choice and they agreed. Oldilocks moved in and actually it did not turn out to be so bad. She cleaned the apartment occasionally and cooked dinner for them every night—a different type of porridge for every day of the week. The Bears liked the honey-flavored porridge. Oldilocks preferred the gin-flavored porridge.

MORAL: *Strindberg Was Right. The Weak Are Stronger Than the Strong. And Ibsen Was Right Too When He Said, "Bears Are Stupid."*

PATSY JUNE IN SUBWAYLAND
(A True Story)

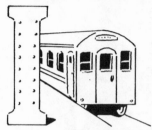

I t was a warm and beautiful spring in Sin City. The ravages of winter were all but forgotten, blotted out of memory by lively, tender green leaves and beauteous forsythia blooms, the cheery songs of birds, and the sunny buzzing of the bees. Sin City was full of renewed life and sunshine and soft breezes; but the people were still their grim, unsmiling, disinterested selves. They traveled vertically in their elevators, silently ignoring each other, made no eye contact with one another as they passed in the streets, and pretended they were completely alone as they shoved their way onto buses and trains.

Enter Patsy June Underhunken from the Hinterlands. Patsy June was an attractive, twenty-year old blonde who had come to Sin City to get into communications and maybe to become the editor of *Vogue* magazine like Diana Vreeland. When Patsy June saw her first subway car she was appalled. "People are so cold here. And unfriendly. I feel it is because they don't know any better. No one has ever just smiled at them and said, 'Hello.' Someone should break the ice and be friendly." Patsy June Underhunken decided that she would be the one to do it.

When the train pulled in and the doors opened, she stepped right in. The first person she came to was a former murderer, currently employed as a short-order crook. Patsy June smiled, extended her hand and said, "Have a nice day." His eyes lit up immediately and the desperado smiled, took Patsy June's hand, and shook it. "Pass it on," said Patsy June and the man turned to the stout, middle-aged shopper next to him and smiled and shook her hand. "Have a nice day," he said. The woman responded in kind. Then she turned to the juvenile members of The Death Squad Social Club, who were sitting across the aisle from her. "Have a nice day,"

47

she smiled, getting up and crossing to their side of the train so she could shake their hands. There were three of them and they were thrilled. No one had ever been nice to them before. They immediately dismantled their .38s, their switch blade knives, and the one bazooka that they shared amongst them.

"Why don't we sing," said Patsy June and she divided the car into three parts. An elegant, slim man with a gray, delicate almost porcelain complexion, who looked as if he drank blood for a living, stood up and began the round. "Row, row, row, your boat, gently down the stream," he sang. Soon the entire car was a rollicking party. Some of the high school girls had joined hands with an entire Chinese family; the Hari Krishnas were dancing to everyone's delight; the Hasidim were dancing right along with them; and the man with the dead dog in his shopping bag, who was crazy and smelled bad to boot, was exchanging phone numbers with the ballet students. When the train stopped no one wanted to leave. Most everyone resolved to ride to the last stop and then take the next train back to their station. Patsy June, however, got off so that she could take another train and spread the good word.

MORAL: *Friendliness Is Contagious. Try It.*

LITTLE JACK HORNER
AND LITTLE MISS MUFFET

ittle Jack Horner, the littlest sadist, decided to have a little night out and he went to the little bar around the corner from where he lived and sat at a tiny table for two where he listened to a little night music. He was joined by Little Miss Muffet, the littlest masochist, who said, "Why, what a surprise to see you here." "Small world," replied the littlest sadist, Little Jack Horner.

Little Jack Horner had a short beer and Little Miss Muffet had a demitasse of espresso. And they made small talk. After a little while, Little Jack Horner called for the little bill, paid it, put down a little tip, and the littlest sadist and the littlest masochist left together. It was a short stroll to the little studio apartment that Little Jack Horner called home. "It isn't much," he said.

Little Jack Horner got out his wee little whips, his cunning little canes, his darling little chains and his dear little thumbscrews. He put Little Miss Muffet on a tuffet and pulled one hair at a time out of her head. "Is that painful?" he asked. "A very little," she answered. "Good," he said.

Then he hung her up on a little wire hanger so that her toes were almost off the floor. He tightened the thumbscrews just a little.

"Do you feel that?" Little Jack Horner asked.

"Not yet," said Little Miss Muffet.

"Well, that's it because I'm winded," said Little Jack Horner.

"Couldn't you make just a little extra effort?" pleaded Little Miss Muffet.

"How little?" asked Little Jack Horner.

"Just a pinch," said Little Miss Muffet.

"Okay, I'll give you a small wound," said Little Jack Horner.

"Could you put some salt in it, please?" begged Little Miss Muffet.

"How much?" said Little Jack Horner.

"Just a pinch," said Little Miss Muffet.

And that's how it went for a few minutes. Little by little, Little Jack Horner, the littlest sadist, caused Little Miss Muffet, the littlest masochist, the littlest amount of pain possible. The littlest sadist had the littlest fun possible; and the littlest masochist had the littlest pleasure possible; and then Little Miss Muffet, the littlest masochist, went home a little early.

MORAL: *A Little Sadism Never Hurts.*

51

DR. JEKYLL AND MR. HYDE ON VACATION

r. Jekyll and Mr. Hyde lived together in Sin City. They were best friends, lived quiet lives, and everyone who knew them liked them. One day, when winter was at its height, Dr. Jekyll said to Mr. Hyde, "It seems like a good time for us to take a little vacation. What do you say to fourteen days someplace sunny and warm?"

"I say, go for it," said Mr. Hyde.

"I'll make the arrangements," said Dr. Jekyll.

A week later the two friends, hearts filled with hope, eyes bright with eager anticipation, set out for their two-week holiday in a carefree world of white beaches, palm trees, coconuts, and dancing beneath the stars. They got as far as the airport, where their plane had a problem leaving the ground. After they had been buckled into their seats an hour and a half, the plane was as stationary as it had been when they boarded it.

"Oh dear," said Dr. Jekyll. "This is not a good beginning for a vacation."

"I think I'll go up front and drop in on the pilot," said Mr. Hyde, and he did so.

Within seconds of Mr. Hyde's visit the 747 moved from its spot, took a position on the runway, and charged into the air. Everyone, the passengers, the stewardesses, the guys in the control tower, was quite surprised, stunned even. Everyone, that is, except Dr. Jekyll and Mr. Hyde. Dr. Jekyll went back to peacefully reading *Psychology Today* and Mr. Hyde went back to sharpening his nails on his teeth.

At the airport in the Third World country of their choice there was a problem leaving the airport. The system for getting a taxicab was seriously disordered and there was a large group of German tourists on line ahead of Dr. Jekyll and Mr. Hyde, who seemed to have mastered it anyway.

"I think I'll go up front and visit the taxi dispatcher," said Mr. Hyde. Within seconds of

53

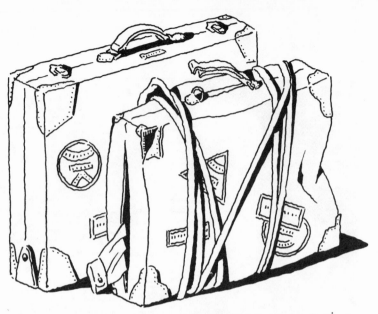

Mr. Hyde's visit, a cab raced to pick up our two vacationers at the end of the line where they stood. As they departed, the German tourists all waved, smiled broadly, and said, "Go with God" in German, their native tongue. Mr. Hyde smiled back and waved the taxi dispatcher's limp hand at them.

The hotel that Dr. Jekyll and Mr. Hyde had chosen had no record of their reservation and was ready to turn them away when Mr. Hyde proved persuasive, if not fatal, to the hotel clerk; and the greedy, overage bellboy rushed them to a room.

The room did not immediately impress. Dr. Jekyll was not sure what it was that annoyed him more: the bat hanging from the light fixture or the straw in the mattress that was sticking through the wormy blanket; but perhaps it was the man from the secret police, who was wearing shoes that showed under the drapes over the only window that looked out on the foreyard of an *abattoir* that really got to him.

"Where do we wash?" he inquired testily. "In the toilet?"

"There is no toilet, but there is running water," said the bellboy. "Over there, from the crack in the wall. If you want to shower I bring a hose, but only between the hours of six and eight in the morning. The electricity goes off after ten at night and only returns at ten the next day. If you want room service, bang a wrench on the pipes," he added, and fled.

"This will never do," said Dr. Jekyll to Mr. Hyde. Mr. Hyde had a short chat with the manager of the hotel and as a result, Dr. Jekyll and Mr. Hyde were given the presidential suite and all the honors and privileges that went with it. The manager of the hotel was given a headache he could not forget. Fortunately he could forget many other things including his name, his address, how to talk, and how to stand up.

From that point on Dr. Jekyll and Mr. Hyde had no more difficulties. Dr. Jekyll spent many golden hours in the sun, basking and tanning, while Mr. Hyde amused himself, especially at night. Both of them had a marvelous time; and on the way back to the airport, Dr. Jekyll was pleased to discover that they had spent no money.

"I've had fourteen perfect days," said Dr. Jekyll.

"And I've committed fourteen perfect crimes," said Mr. Hyde. "Let's come back next year."

The next year when vacation time came around, Dr. Jekyll and Mr. Hyde returned to their tropical paradise. Unfortunately for them, Mr. Hyde was recognized as last year's homicidal maniac; and they were arrested at the airport as they were claiming their baggage. It cost them three thousand dollars apiece to buy their freedom and they were told they had to leave the country at once. Their vacation was ruined.

MORAL: *You Cannot Step In The Same River of Blood Twice.*

THE PRINCESS AND THE FLEA

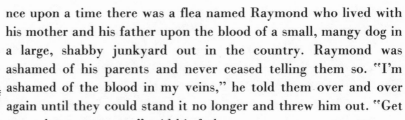

nce upon a time there was a flea named Raymond who lived with his mother and his father upon the blood of a small, mangy dog in a large, shabby junkyard out in the country. Raymond was ashamed of his parents and never ceased telling them so. "I'm ashamed of the blood in my veins," he told them over and over again until they could stand it no longer and threw him out. "Get off and stay off. And never come home anymore," said his father.

And so Raymond went to Sin City looking to better his blood.

His visit coincided with that of the Princess Luciana Saxe-Taxe Von Guernsey Di Rienzi of Trufflestein, a small and seldom visited principality in Central Europe. The princess could trace her royal bloodlines back to prefeudal times. In her veins flowed at least a trace of all the royal blood of Europe: a bit of Elizabeth, Peter, Eleanor, Henry, Ludwig, Charlemagne, Harold, two great Catherines, Attila, Caligula, and even a few popes.

The Royal Imperial Hotel, on the other hand, was fairly new. It had been in business a mere seventy-five years; and the only royal blood it could claim had been shed in one of its bathrooms by the very excited and depressed pretender to the throne of Togo Land, when he cut himself shaving in 1956. Nevertheless, the hotel enjoyed a spotless reputation. Its service was flawless and the attitude of its staff was unimpeachably haughty and regal. And that is why the Princess Luciana and Raymond both chose to stay there when they visited the city.

On the morning of her last day at the Royal Imperial the princess awoke to discover an unprecedented red welt on the soft white skin of her upper left bicep.

A doctor was sent for. "This is a flea's bite," he pronounced.

"What is a flea?" asked the princess.

"A flea is a louse," answered the doctor.

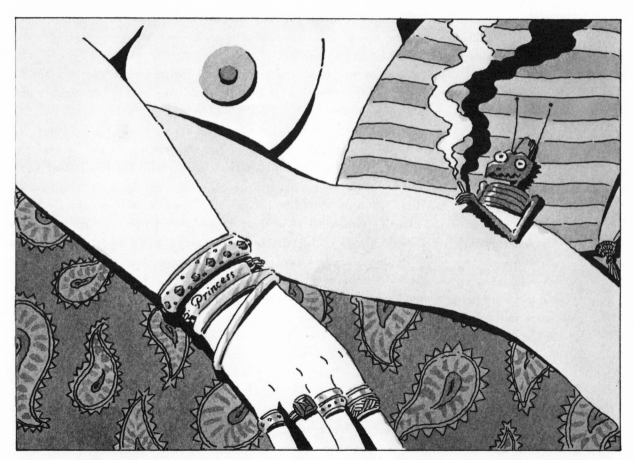

"If you make that plural does that come out as lice?" asked the princess.

"Yes," replied the doctor.

The horrified princess refused to pay her bill.

The horrified management of the Royal Imperial Hotel insisted that she pay her bill, claimed that she herself had brought the flea to the hotel, and confiscated her luggage in an effort to ensure that she would pay her bill.

The dispute became a *cause célèbre*. Newspapers and scandal sheets had a field day. The hotel was referred to as the "Royal Imperial Fleabag" and the princess as the "Royal Flea-bag." Neither was pleased. Suits and countersuits were filed. Finally they had their day in court.

The Royal Imperial Hotel was represented by the powerful law firm of Hunt and Peck, who took the precaution of planting strange fleas in the princess' luggage to "further the truth." The luggage was opened at the trial and the strange fleas emerged, and they turned the courtroom into a circus. The Princess Luciana Saxe-Taxe Von Guernsey Di Rienzi was humiliated—and lost her case besides. She returned to her homeland a broken princess with a Band-Aid on her arm and *disgrace* engraved upon her heart. Not long afterwards she died of a mysterious lingering ailment, not unlike dog fever.

The Royal Imperial Hotel suffered a terrific decline in business and never again had a royal visitor. Instead, they were forced to cater to conventions.

Meanwhile, Mrs. Defarge, the head housekeeper, was getting the princess' old room, which had been sealed and unoccupied throughout the entire brouhaha, ready for new guests, when what to her wondering eyes should appear, luxuriating on the pink silk bedclothes once slept in by the Princess Luciana, but a very small and self-satisifed flea, who told her that his name was Raymond the First.

Mrs. Defarge put her hand out in order to snatch up Raymond and squeeze him out of existence.

"Ah, ah, ah, you don't want to do that," said Raymond. "I'm the flea that did in Luciana and there is royal blood in my veins now." He lay back on the pillows with a self-satisfied smirk. Mrs. Defarge studied him for a few minutes and then she put out her hand and squeezed him out of existence.

MORAL: *Take Pride in Your Humble Origins, Peasants. Down Through the Ages It Has Never Been Safe to Be Of Royal Blood.*

METAMORPHOSIS II

ne bright Thursday morning in July a cockroach awoke to discover that he had been turned into a man named Gregory Samson. Instantly terror raced through him and he ran blindly around the room looking for a crack in which to hide. He was too big to get behind the baseboard. He tried to climb the wall to get behind the cornice over the window and fell back repeatedly. Finally, embarrassed by his nudity, he put on clothing and then, as long as he was wearing a three-piece suit with a necktie and white shirt, he decided to try going to work.

The subway was a terrific shock to his system. And very noisy. He crawled along the floor sadly and remembered the sweet peace and quiet of the garbage trap just under the sink drain. A woman watching him thought that he had lost a contact lens and joined him on the floor to help look for it. "I found it," she said, holding up something she had found under a piece of chewing gum. Gregory said, "Thank you," and put it in his mouth and swallowed it. The woman got off the subway at the next stop.

Gregory went to an office, sat down at a desk, and started moving papers around. Someone came up to him and said, "What are you doing?" "I'm working," he replied, and the person went away and left him alone.

During lunch break, he joined three other men from the office. The men asked him what he was going to order and he said, "Nothing, I'll just finish what you leave behind. I don't like hot food," he explained. He ended up having a half lettuce leaf, seven sticks of french-fried-potatoes, and a large quantity of ketchup which he scooped up with his finger. The three men looked at him suspiciously. Gregory felt nervous, and so he lifted his arms straight in the air and waved them back and forth. The three men now stared at him, not knowing what to think. Gregory smiled nonchalantly and polished off the contents of one entire sugar dispens-

er. The three men stood up in order to make a run for it and get away from Gregory when their attention was distracted by a roach that was ascending the wall of the restaurant. "Uccch!" said one of the men. "I always thought this was a dirty restaurant." He slammed his hand up against the wall and crushed the poor roach to death. "That was my sister," said Gregory Samson, and he began to cry. The three men quietly edged their way towards the door. Gregory, suddenly seized with uncontrollable rage, ran after them and discovered with great pleasure a use for the big, hard teeth that filled his mouth.

MORAL: *People Don't Kill. Teeth Do.*

THE BANK CRISIS

The whole tragic episode took place on a Friday morning. The Bilberry Bank opened as usual at 8:30. By 11 o'clock there were five windows functioning and three customers on line. At 11:10, teller, Harriet Scaglione, closed down temporarily to count her money. She discovered that she had five dollars too much in her cash drawer.

"This ain't right," she said, and turned to the teller next to her. "Oh, Dave," she said. "Could you help me, I'm five dollars over in my cash drawer."

Dave closed his window and went over to her. "Let's go through all your money," he said and began counting. "Hey," he said, "you ain't over five, you is over seven."

"I double-checked," she said. "It can't be seven, it's gotta be five."

"Let's call in Fred," said Dave. Fred closed his window and came over to help out. There were now sixteen people in line and two windows open. One of the windows was occupied with a business deposit, which normally lasted forever, but was taking even longer this Friday.

Fred counted the money and told Harriet and Dave that, "There is six dollars too much in this drawer."

"You don't say," said Dave. "Gee, I checked it out and I got seven."

"And I came out five," said Harriet.

"Hey, look at that," said Dave, pointing to the line, which had grown to twenty-five people. It was 12:24.

"Don't mind them," said Harriet. "We got a real problem here." She turned to Tanya, another teller. "Hey, Tanya," she yelled. "When you finish with that bozo, would you come over here? We got a problem."

Tanya closed down and came over. She counted all the bills and all the change. "I make it you're four dollars over."

"What do we do now?" asked Harriet.

"Let's wait for Bill," said Tanya. "He'll straighten everything out."

At 1:30, when Bill had finished with the interminable business deposit, he joined the tellers at Harriet's cash drawer and slowly and carefully counted the money. Meanwhile there were now no windows open and the line had grown to over a hundred angry and red-faced people. They pressed against the imitation velvet crowd-control rope. Some shook their fists in rage at the windows.

Mr. Olgin, the manager, came out from behind his desk.

"Kill him," someone shouted. "No, no!" said older, wiser heads.

Mr. Olgin raised his arms to the crowd in a placating manner.

"Please be patient," he said. "The Bilberry Bank loves you. Our motto is, 'The small depositor is the cornerstone of big banking.'"

"I'll cornerstone you in a minute!" screamed one of the more irate customers, and he ran toward the cornerstone of the building. Several others rushed to help him. Together they pulled the massive granite rock out of its corner and the entire bank collapsed. It was just 3 o'clock. Closing time.

MORAL: *Money Is the Root of All Evil.*

THE WOMAN WHO NEEDED HELP

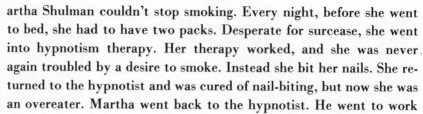

artha Shulman couldn't stop smoking. Every night, before she went to bed, she had to have two packs. Desperate for surcease, she went into hypnotism therapy. Her therapy worked, and she was never again troubled by a desire to smoke. Instead she bit her nails. She returned to the hypnotist and was cured of nail-biting, but now she was an overeater. Martha went back to the hypnotist. He went to work on her, and after three sessions she gave up over-eating. However, in the ensuing two weeks she drank seventeen quarts of whiskey. Once again she went back for treatment. Once again she was cured. Once again she developed a new compulsion: not sleeping. Once again she returned to the hypnotist. Once again the hypnotism worked. She found she could sleep fine, but not alone. Martha became an ecstatic fornicator and she never went back to the hypnotist again. Ever.

MORAL: *When You Are Finished With Therapy No One Has To Tell You, You Will Know It.*

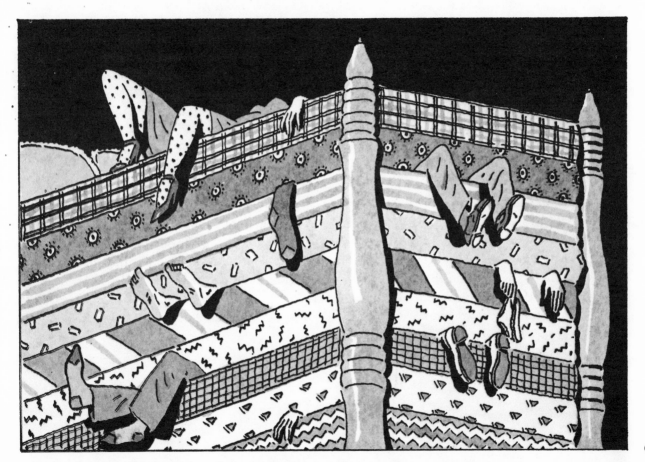

THE OLD WOMAN AND THE HOODLUMS

There was once an old, frail, little woman who lived upstairs from a candy store that catered to a band of teenaged boys who wore bloodstained bandannas around their heads, artfully torn T-shirts beneath artfully torn, hand-painted denim jackets, and sunglasses after dark because the night hurt their eyes. They congregated every evening to fight, jostle, dance, sing, play their radios at top volume, and hallucinate on various combinations of drugs.

The noise they made bothered the old, frail, little woman and she tried everything to make them stop making it. She complained to the police, who did nothing; she complained to the superintendent, who did nothing; she complained to the boys themselves, but they, fortunately, did nothing because they couldn't hear her over the noise.

One day she came home from feeding the pigeons that lived on the traffic island near her house, and as she opened the door to her apartment and stepped inside, she found herself face-to-face with a burglar. Quickly she slammed the door and ran out into the street shouting, "Help! Help!" Immediately all the hoodlums ran away because they had street smarts and knew that when there is trouble near you, the wisest course of action is to split. After that the old, frail, little woman cried, "Help!" whenever she needed a little peace and quiet. And it always worked.

MORAL: *Help! Is Its Own Help.*

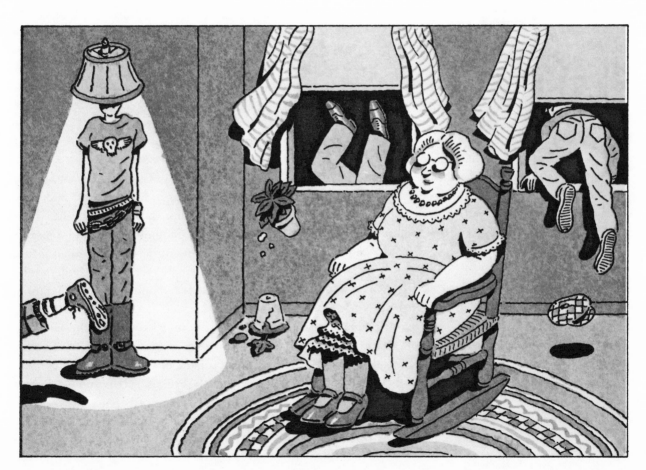

69

CINDERANNIE

nce upon a time there was a shopping-bag lady named Cinderannie, who lived with her wicked stepmother and her two wicked stepsisters. She sat around in the cinders of the fireplace most of the time and never had to clean or iron clothing, because everything she touched became incredibly filthy in no time. One day it was announced that the King was giving a big party to introduce his son to everybody. The wicked stepmother and the two wicked stepsisters were going, but Cinderannie had to stay at home because they wouldn't take her with them; they were ashamed of her.

After her stepmother and her two stepsisters left for the big party, Cinderannie sat around in the coals and wept because she really wanted to go, and she was feeling left out. Suddenly her Fairy Godmother appeared before her and promised to send her to the King's affair. Cinderannie and her Fairy Godmother rummaged around in her shopping bags and found a pumpkin, four mice, a fat lizard, and a fatter rat. The Fairy Godmother turned them into a coach, four horses, a footman, and a driver, in that order. Then she turned to Cinderannie. "You can't go looking like that," she said and waved her magic wand and turned Cinderannie into a clean, well-dressed, perfectly coiffed, bejeweled woman.

When Cinderannie arrived at the ball, she looked around her and liked what she saw. She saw an empty Perrier bottle sitting on a table and, since there were no pockets in her ball gown, she tucked the bottle into her bodice. She found half a pack of Camels on the floor and tucked them into the top of her stockings. She found a slightly broken earring under a chair and tucked it into her off-the-shoulder puffed sleeve, and threw a coffeepot in there, too, which after a while leaked serious stains down her arm and side. She noticed a pair of woman's shoes under a table and grabbed them. They were made for feet larger than her own, so she put them on over her shoes. After she filled the pockets of the man's tuxedo jacket that she

71

had grabbed along the way and put on, she rummaged around in a closet and found a large plastic garbage bag, which she attached to her waist and began filling up with left-over food. All this in time to the music. Never in her life had Cinderannie had such fun. She did not leave at midnight as she had been warned to do, but when her coach turned into a pumpkin, and her horses turned into mice, and her footman turned into a lizard, and her driver turned into a rat, she scooped them up and tucked them into her bag.

By this time her antics had drawn attention to her and she felt that all eyes were upon her. This was true. She looked across the crowd of faces and saw three familiar ones: the faces of her wicked stepmother and her two wicked stepsisters.

"Hi!" she waved. "Look at all the good stuff I'm getting. I'll show you everything when we get back home."

Cinderannie's wicked stepmother and her two wicked stepsisters gave out biting little shrieks and fainted because they knew they were ruined socially forever.

MORAL: *Living Well Is the Best Revenge.*